An Introduction to Low Temperature Differential Stirling Engines

JAMES   R.   SENFT

Moriya Press

Copyright © 1996 James R. Senft

ISBN 0-9652455-1-9

Fourth Printing 2000

Cover illustration: a drawing by Josip Antonic´
of the author's P-19 engine running on
the warmth of a hand.

Bless the Lord, all works of the Lord,

sing praise to him and highly exalt him for ever.

Daniel 3:35

An Introduction to Low Temperature Differential Stirling Engines

I. Origin and Development

In recent years, understanding of the Stirling engine has enjoyed considerable growth. Research and development on the Stirling engine has steadily progressed, and many new insights, inventions, and potential applications have been discovered and explored. One of the most exciting recent developments is the so-called "low temperature differential" Stirling engine. This new type of Stirling is capable of running on very small differences in temperature between the hot and cold sides, or better to say, between the warm and cool sides. Low temperature differential Stirling engines have been built that run on differentials ranging from just under 100°C (180°F) down to an incredible 1/2°C (1°F).[1] This means that Stirling engines can now utilize low grade heat sources for their operation ranging from passive solar or geothermal energy to industrial process waste heat. Whether LTD [2] Stirling engines can be put to practical use is an open question and still the subject of ongoing research and development work which is being carried out worldwide at universities, government laboratories, and in the private sector.

What was quite clear from the very beginning of our work on LTD engines is that in model sizes they excel in educational value. They show and teach what a heat engine is and how a Stirling engine

---

[1] In this book, the Celsius (or Centigrade) temperature will usually be given and the Fahrenheit equivalent given in parentheses where helpful. The relationship between the units in the two scales is that each Fahrenheit degree equals five ninths of a Celsius degree.

[2] LTD will be used for "low temperature differential" in this book

works perhaps better than anything else. They can be operated almost anywhere: in a classroom or lecture hall, in a meeting room or plush corporate board room, and in the kitchen or the parlor. Placed atop a cup of hot coffee or just held in warm hands, a running LTD engine demonstrates the conversion of thermal energy into mechanical energy in a way that is easy to observe and study . Furthermore, LTD engines are simple enough to be constructed in a school shop or in a fairly well equipped home workshop from materials that are relatively easy to obtain and work with.

This book is intended to introduce the field of LTD engines. Assuming no special background,[1] it aims to describe what they are, where they came from, the physics behind them, why they developed as they did, what can be learned from them, and how they are made. A great deal can be learned by observing a real operating LTD engine, and even more by making a LTD engine from scratch. For those readers having access to a shop, the second part of the book contains drawings and directions for making a LTD engine which will effortlessly run on the heat of your hand. The engine is in fact a replica of an engine custom designed and built by the author for NASA in 1992. It was used by the space agency to demonstrate and explain the basic concepts and characteristics of a much more sophisticated Stirling engine that they are developing for generating electric power for space stations and planetary bases from solar or nuclear energy. The book includes a list of sources of materials and components for engine builders, and a long list of references to books, technical papers, and articles on the subject of LTD engines for further study.

The Development of Low Temperature Differential Stirling Engines

In the spring of 1983, Prof. Ivo Kolin of the University of Zagreb in Croatia[2] pleasantly startled the Stirling engine world by

---

[1] Nevertheless, a basic knowledge of the material on Stirling engines covered in the author's book *An Introduction to Stirling Engines* would be helpful.
[2] formerly part of Yugoslavia

publicly exhibiting an engine running on the heat of boiling hot water. The setting was at a short course on Stirling engines taught by Prof. Kolin, Prof. Walker, and myself at the Inter University Center in the historic coastal city of Dubrovnik. While Prof. Kolin described to the audience the engine that he had been developing for about three years, his wife, Vlasta, devotedly poured boiling hot water into one compartment of the engine and cold water into another. After a minute or so, Ivo turned the flywheel once and the engine began to run, much to the amazement of us all .

At the time, 100°C in itself was an incredibly low temperature difference for a Stirling engine to run on. It was all the more astonishing that the engine continued to run for a long time at lower and lower temperature differentials between the water reservoirs. Running slower and slower as the hot water cooled down and the cool water warmed up, the engine finally came to a complete stop when the temperature differential dropped below about 20°C (36°F) .

Prof. Kolin's engine was built entirely with hand tools. It featured a square displacer chamber and a rubber diaphragm in place of a piston and cylinder. The Styrofoam displacer was 20 cm (7-7/8 in)[1] square. A unique feature of this engine was a "slip link" drive for the displacer which gave it an intermittent motion; this type of motion is thermally beneficial in slow moving engines. A speed of 50 rpm was typical for his engine with a temperature difference of 50°C in its reservoirs. This first LTD engine is completely described in Ivo Kolin's book *Isothermal Stirling Cycle Engine* which even includes fully dimensioned drawings (in metric units) so that anyone interested can make an exact replica.

In the fall of 1983, the first Ringbom type of LTD Stirling engine was designed and built by the author while a visiting scientist at Argonne National Laboratory. This engine design introduced a round horizontally oriented displacer chamber which could be placed over a container of hot water for the heat source. The displacer of the engine

---

[1] For exact conversion , one inch equals 2.54 centimeters

was about 8.5" in diameter and was driven by a small piston and cylinder unit to give an intermittent motion with a phasing that varied with the engine speed. The main piston drive featured a rocking lever which freed the piston of virtually all side loading for low friction and wear.

This first LTD Ringbom engine was extensively tested and yielded a number of new insights. This engine taught us a great deal about LTD Stirling engines, about the subtleties of Ringbom engine operation, and about the mechanical efficiency of heat engines in general. The main details of the engine's construction and test results can be found in the author's book *Ringbom Stirling Engines* and the technical papers and articles listed in the References section at the end of this book.

The Argonne engine proved to be a good demonstrator of Stirling engine operation. With about two cups of near boiling hot water poured into the lower insulated reservoir, and a like amount of ice water in a pan placed on top of the displacer chamber, the engine starts in a matter of seconds and will run for about an hour. When set to a low compression ratio, the engine will run at a temperature differential of 7°C . The engine still resides at the laboratory under the watchful care of senior scientist Dr. Paul Roach where it is a favorite attraction for visitors and school children who tour the lab from time to time.

From these first two engines, Prof. Kolin and the author worked in parallel over the next decade each developing a series of LTD engines. Included in the author's line are the "L-27" solar Ringbom engine[1], the "P-19" ultra low temperature differential engine[2], and the "N-92" NASA demonstration engine [3] whose construction is described in the second part of this book.

---

[1] Constructed in 1986
[2] Constructed in 1990
[3] Constructed in 1992

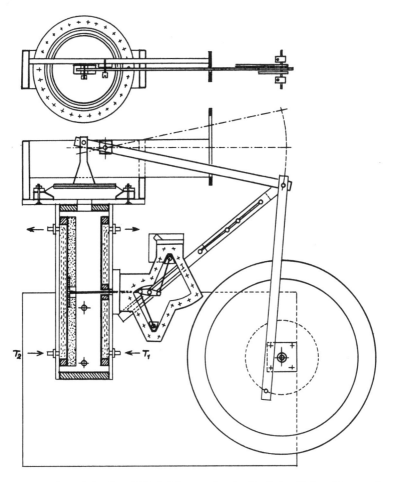

A scale drawing of the first LTD Stirling engine by Prof. Ivo Kolin. The engine was built entirely with hand tools using common materials and standard hardware items. Instead of a piston and cylinder, this engine used a round rubber diaphragm which is worked by a long lever linked to the crankshaft. Below the diaphragm unit is the displacer chamber of the engine. This is basically a short plexiglas box with two inner water reservoirs. These reservoirs have metal plate faces inside and the polystyrene foam displacer oscillates between these plates. The displacer rod is connected to a Watt straight line linkage system which is enclosed within a special narrow housing extending from the main displacer chamber.

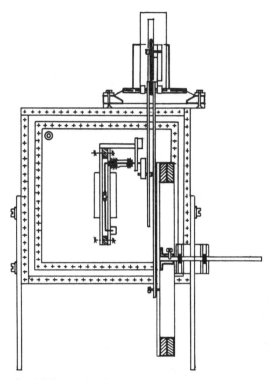

A view of the first Kolin engine from the crankshaft end. The largest square is the outline of the main chamber. Its frame is visible through the clear plexiglas ends. The nearest water reservoir is also visible as the slightly smaller square unit. The crosses show the location of the multitude of screws used to ensure the air-tightness of the chambers. LTD engines do not tolerate much leakage. The screws entered tapped holes in the plexiglas frame and rubber gaskets were used for seals. The narrowness of the Watt linkage housing can be seen in this view which of course was adopted to minimize dead space. The axle of the upper swinging arm of the Watt linkage exits the housing and is ingeniously sealed against air leakage by a soft rubber torsion tube. On the outer end of this axle is an arm which is driven by a slotted link. The thick-rimmed flywheel carries the single crankpin, and the main shaft runs in ball bearings. This engine was first publicly exhibited and demonstrated at the Inter University Center in Dubrovnik in 1983. These drawings by Prof. Kolin are reproduced here very near to one-fifth of actual size.

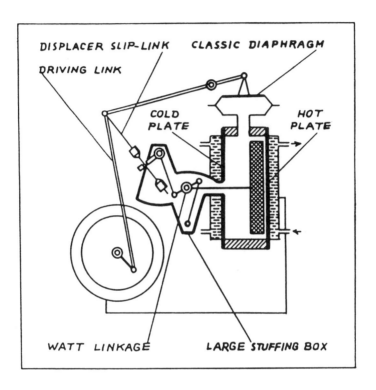

DISPLACER SLIP-LINK   CLASSIC DIAPHRAGM

DRIVING LINK

COLD PLATE

HOT PLATE

WATT LINKAGE   LARGE STUFFING BOX

This schematic drawing by Prof. Kolin illustrates the main features of the first LTD engine. It clearly shows the nature of the "slip-link" system used to drive the displacer. The slip link imparts an intermittent motion to the displacer whereby it makes its strokes rapidly and then dwells in place against one of the reservoir plates. Basically, this quickly puts and then keeps the engine air in the right place at the right time and results in a good thermodynamic cycle for the engine. This type of displacer motion is very effective at the low speeds characteristic of LTD engines.

The first Ringbom type LTD Stirling engine. This engine was designed by the author and built at Argonne National Laboratory in the fall of 1983. This engine first introduced the round horizontally oriented displacer chamber which made it possible to place the engine over a reservoir of hot water for operation. The engine was capable of running at a temperature differential as low as 7°C (13°F). To obtain larger temperature differences for higher power operation, a pan is placed on the top cold plate of the engine and filled with ice water. At a temperature difference of 80°C (144°F), this engine had a peak shaft power of just over 1 Watt at about 125 rpm. The Ringbom is a type of Stirling engine in which the displacer is driven by a small piston rather than through a mechanical linkage from the crankshaft. This second piston is attached directly to the displacer and is so proportioned that it moves the displacer in the right way for the engine to run as a Stirling engine. The Ringbom drive system produces the type of intermittent motion that is ideally suited for LTD engines. (Photo by Argonne National laboratory)

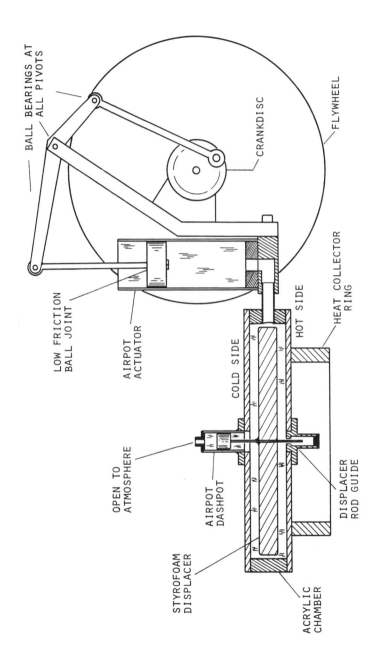

BALL BEARINGS AT ALL PIVOTS

CRANKDISC

FLYWHEEL

LOW FRICTION BALL JOINT

AIRPOT ACTUATOR

HEAT COLLECTOR RING

HOT SIDE

COLD SIDE

OPEN TO ATMOSPHERE

AIRPOT DASHPOT

DISPLACER ROD GUIDE

STYROFOAM DISPLACER

ACRYLIC CHAMBER

A schematic scale drawing of the first LTD Ringbom engine.

A close-up view of the mechanical section of the first LTD Ringbom engine. The cylinder is glass with a graphite piston that is manufactured by the Airpot Corporation. A lever drive for the piston rod was chosen to minimize the side forces imposed upon the piston to reduce friction and wear. The connecting rod end of the lever was made shorter to reduce the size of the crank and to allow the configuration to be "bent" into a very compact arrangement . (Photo by Argonne National Laboratory)

This close-up of the 1983 LTD Ringbom engine shows the cold water pan in place on top of the engine. It is a standard 9" pie pan with a hole cut in the center to clear the small Airpot cylinder unit which drives the displacer. The length of the plexiglas tubing which is cemented over the hole is generous to prevent the accidental splashing of water into the displacer drive cylinder. (Photo by Argonne National Laboratory)

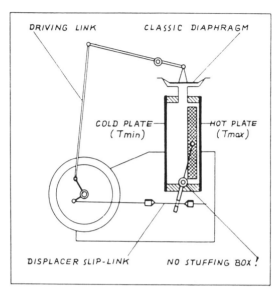

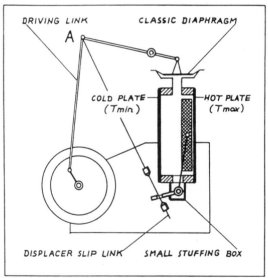

Schematic drawings of two engines designed by Prof. Kolin in 1984. Each employs the diaphragm as used on the first LTD engine but have significantly simpler displacer drive systems. The torsion tube seal and is again featured on these engines. (Drawings by Kolin)

12

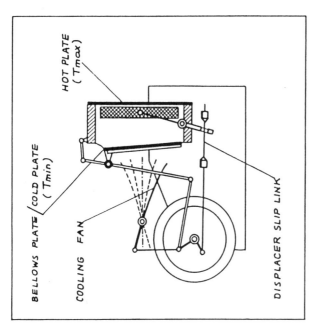

HOT PLATE (T_{max})

BELLOWS PLATE / COLD PLATE (T_{min})

COOLING FAN

DISPLACER SLIP LINK

Subsequent engines by Prof. Kolin in 1985 and 1986 incorporated the diaphragm into the cold end of the engine. The cold plate is surrounded by a rubber membrane in such a way that the plate can move as though hinged along its bottom edge. This makes a separate diaphragm unit unnecessary and is especially suited to air cooling.

This small Ringbom LTD engine was designed and built by the author in 1985. Nicknamed the "L-27" , this engine was sponsored by the Charles A. Lindbergh Foundation to investigate operation on solar energy. The engine operates at speeds over 700 rpm and can maintain operation on a temperature difference of 5°C (9°F).

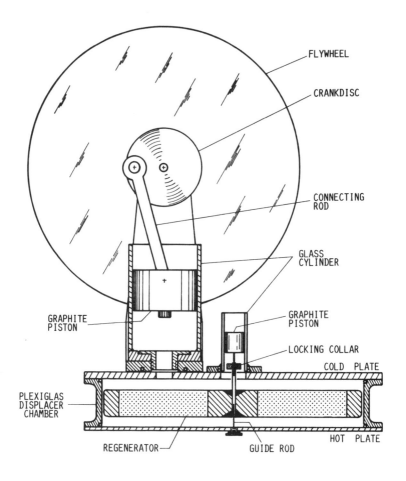

FLYWHEEL

CRANKDISC

CONNECTING
ROD

GLASS
CYLINDER

GRAPHITE
PISTON

GRAPHITE
PISTON

LOCKING COLLAR

COLD PLATE

PLEXIGLAS
DISPLACER
CHAMBER

REGENERATOR

GUIDE ROD

HOT PLATE

A scale sectional drawing of the L-27.   The displacer of this engine is 5.1" in
diameter and incorporates regenerator elements for improved efficiency and
higher speed operation.

The L-27 engine operating on solar energy. A conical reflector gathers in solar energy and directs it to the engine hot plate which is coated with a black absorptive paint and covered with a plexiglas window. Since the conical type of reflector does not focus to a point, it need not constantly track the sun for good operation, but only requires adjusting the aim every hour or so. The engine is fitted here with a finned cold plate to improve convective cooling.

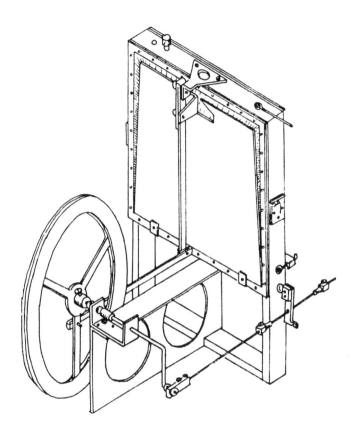

Detail drawing by Prof. Kolin of one of his later moving cold plate LTD engines
of greatly simplified construction.

This photograph shows a tiny Ringbom LTD engine, the "L-77", built by the author in 1989 alongside the L-27 engine.

18

Beginning in 1989, one hundred of these LTD Ringbom Stirling engines based on the L-27 engine were produced by Rob McConaghy's New Machine Company. These engines were manufactured to high standards and performed very well.

The "P-19" is an ultra low temperature difference Stirling engine designed and built by the author at the University of Wisconsin in River Falls. Completed in the spring of 1990, it proved itself capable of operating at a temperature differential of only one half of a Celsius degree (just under one degree Fahrenheit). The compression ratio of the engine is a mere 1.004 to 1.

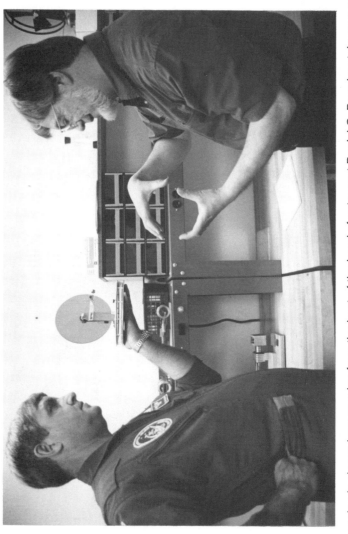

The P-19 engine is shown here running from the heat of the hand of astronaut Daniel C. Brandenstein on a recent visit to the University of Wisconsin at River Falls. The character on the right is the author, talking about Stirling engines as usual. The P-19 easily runs at over 100 rpm when hand held. If the engine is placed on an insulated pad, it continues to run on the thermal energy in its warm plate for about 15 minutes.

A cold drink placed on the upper plate of the P-19 engine is enough run it for
an hour or so.

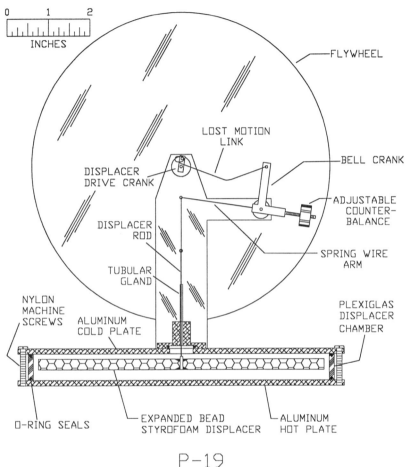

0   1   2
INCHES

FLYWHEEL

LOST MOTION
LINK

DISPLACER
DRIVE CRANK

BELL CRANK

ADJUSTABLE
COUNTER-
BALANCE

DISPLACER
ROD

SPRING WIRE
ARM

TUBULAR
GLAND

NYLON
MACHINE
SCREWS

ALUMINUM
COLD PLATE

PLEXIGLAS
DISPLACER
CHAMBER

O-RING SEALS

EXPANDED BEAD
STYROFOAM DISPLACER

ALUMINUM
HOT PLATE

P-19
AN ULTRA LOW TEMPERATURE DIFFERENTIAL
STIRLING ENGINE

This scale schematic drawing of the P-19 Stirling engine shows the lost motion linkage system for driving the displacer. This produces an intermittent movement of the displacer which is effective at low speeds. The weight of the displacer is counterbalanced to minimize friction loss in the engine mechanism. These features are important for operation at ultra low temperature differentials.

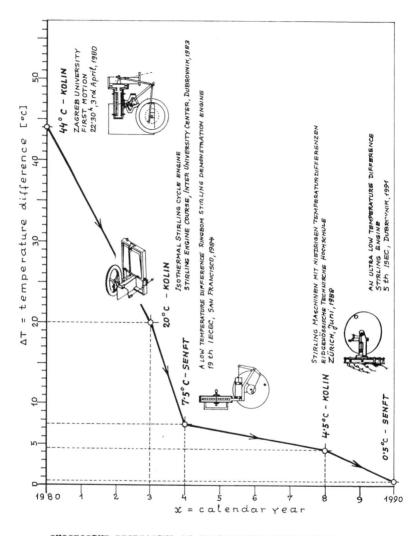

SUCCESSIVE DECREASING OF TEMPERATURE DIFFERENCE

This chart by Prof. Kolin presents a capsule history of the first decade of LTD Stirling engine research and development.

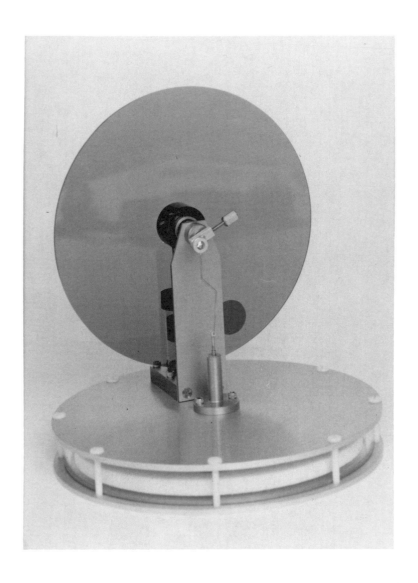

This is the "N-92" engine which was designed and built by the author for NASA. Its design is optimized for hand held operation. Full details on how to make this engine are presented in the second part of this book.

This is a very rough and ready engine made by the author in 1992 to demonstrate how simply an engine can be built that will run on the warmth of a hand.

Shown here is the second LTD engine manufactured by the New Machine Company. Production of this engine began in 1993. This engine will efficiently run on warm tap water or ice water placed in its insulated base.

Who says that LTD engines can't do anything? The author made this device to "prove" the contrary. Geared to the shaft of a New Machine Co. engine is a crank carrying an arm with a gong on its end. A stub shaft protruding from the crank picks up the gong arm and lifts it half a revolution until it goes over center. Then the gong swings down and sounds the bell. With ice in the base reservoir, the engine will persistently ring the bell for hours on end!

II. Theory and Operation

The Components of LTD Stirling Engines

The components of a LTD Stirling engine are identical in character to those of a conventional Stirling engine. The only differences are in the relative proportions of the engine parts. Figure 1 is a schematic representation of an LTD engine capable of operating at quite a low differential in temperature between the hot and the cold sections. The major components shown in the illustration are exactly those to be found in any Stirling engine of the split-cylinder or gamma type.

All but one of the components in Fig. 1 are devices with which anyone of a mechanical bent is familiar. The exception may be the item labeled as the "displacer". The displacer usually takes the same form as a piston, but its purpose is not to compress or expand the engine air. In the illustration here it is purposely depicted as not being a close fit in its cylinder. There is ample space for air to flow around it as it is made to reciprocate within its chamber. Its function is to take up space within the chamber so that whichever way it is moved, the air goes around it to the other side. In this way it is possible to move air back and forth inside the engine chamber.

The displacer chamber has one end heated and the other cooled. Connected to the displacer section is a piston and cylinder unit, which compresses and expands the engine air in the usual way. There is a linkage between the piston, displacer, and the crankshaft which phases the reciprocation of the displacer about ninety degrees ahead of that of the piston in the direction of rotation. Every split-cylinder Stirling engine has these essential components. The bellcrank linkage system used in Fig. 1 is just one example of many possible mechanisms which are suitable. [1]

---

[1] The first chapter of the book *Ringbom Stirling Engines* contains a general treatment of the mechanism problem for Stirling engines.

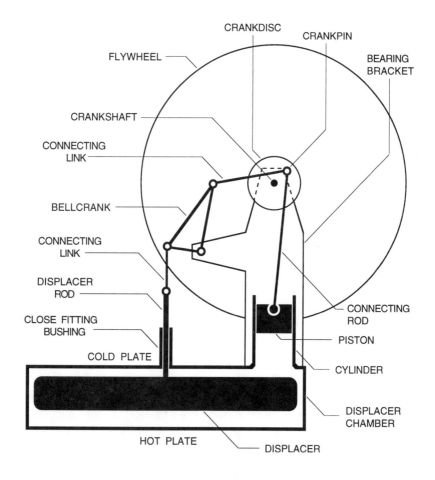

Fig. 1 Sectional view of a low temperature differential Stirling engine

How LTD Stirling Engines Work

The cycle of operation of a LTD engine is identical to that of a conventional Stirling engine. The four basic steps of the operating cycle of the engine of Fig. 1 are depicted in Figs. 2 through 5. Each of the figures represents a quarter turn of the crankshaft during which a certain thermodynamic process predominately occurs within the engine. In Fig. 2, the piston is going through its reversal near its innermost dead center. During this ninety degrees of crank rotation, namely from 45° before inner dead center to 45° after, the piston does not move very much. It goes from a little above bottom dead center down to exact bottom dead center and then back up a little from bottom dead center. If you know your trigonometry, a minute or two of calculation will show that during this whole quarter turn the piston is never farther away from bottom dead center than about 15% of its total stroke.[1] So the volume of the air inside the engine changes very little, or is nearly constant.

Now look at what the displacer is doing during this quarter turn. The bellcrank linkage, as pointed out before, puts the displacer 90° out of phase from the piston. Therefore while the piston is more or less idling around its inner dead center, the displacer is passing right through the middle of its stroke. And therefore it's making its move relatively fast. The same trigonometry as before shows that in fact it travels about 70% [2] of its full stroke during this quarter revolution of the crankshaft. Because of the clearance around the displacer, as it moves, the air in the chamber goes around it and finds itself on the other side of the engine. Thus practically all of the air that was on the cold side is moved next to the hot plate during this quarter turn. Thermal energy flows from the hot plate into the cooler air now next to it, and the air warms up.

---

[1] The exact fraction is $\frac{1}{2}\left(1 - \frac{\sqrt{2}}{2}\right) = 0.146...$

[2] The exact fraction is $\frac{1}{\sqrt{2}} = 0.707...$

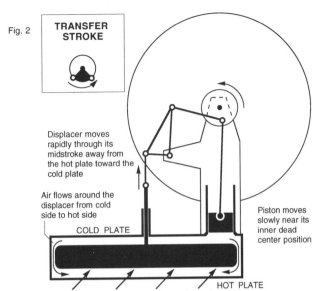

Fig. 2

TRANSFER STROKE

Displacer moves rapidly through its midstroke away from the hot plate toward the cold plate

Air flows around the displacer from cold side to hot side

COLD PLATE

Piston moves slowly near its inner dead center position

HOT PLATE

Heat flows in to raise the temperature of the air entering the hot section of the displacer chamber

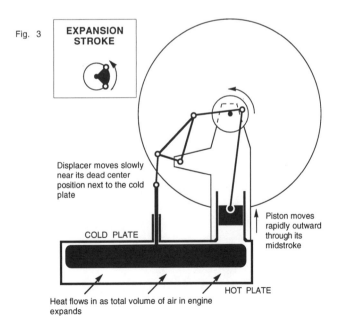

Fig. 3

EXPANSION STROKE

Displacer moves slowly near its dead center position next to the cold plate

COLD PLATE

Piston moves rapidly outward through its midstroke

HOT PLATE

Heat flows in as total volume of air in engine expands

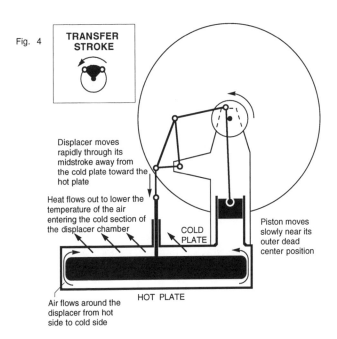

Fig. 4

TRANSFER STROKE

Displacer moves rapidly through its midstroke away from the cold plate toward the hot plate

Heat flows out to lower the temperature of the air entering the cold section of the displacer chamber

COLD PLATE

Piston moves slowly near its outer dead center position

Air flows around the displacer from hot side to cold side

HOT PLATE

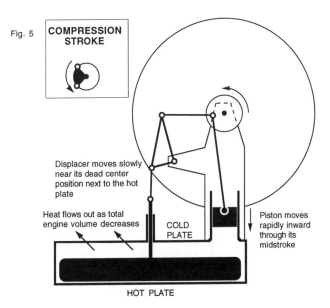

Fig. 5

COMPRESSION STROKE

Displacer moves slowly near its dead center position next to the hot plate

Heat flows out as total engine volume decreases

COLD PLATE

Piston moves rapidly inward through its midstroke

HOT PLATE

33

This analysis clearly shows that during this quarter turn of the crank the following thermal process occurs: without much compression or expansion, most of the air within the engine is transferred from the cold side to the hot side, it warms up, and accordingly its pressure rises. This is one of the so-called "transfer" strokes of the Stirling engine cycle, and its main effect is simply to heat up most of the air in the engine. The mechanical energy required for the piston and displacer to move during this part of the cycle is small and comes from the rotating flywheel.

Now in Fig. 3 the movements of the piston and the displacer are just the opposite in character. Here the piston goes through most of its outward stroke - again about 70% of it - and is pushed by the elevated pressure within the engine. This is the "expansion" stroke during which the piston delivers work to the crankshaft, and it delivers more than it took from the flywheel during the previous transfer stroke. The surplus can do work outside the engine. Meanwhile, the displacer is rounding its upper dead center and so stays near the cold plate. This keeps most of the air in the displacer chamber near the hot plate from which it continues to absorb heat as the piston carries out its expansion. Throughout the expansion stroke, the pressure steadily drops within the engine until just near the end of stroke the pressure is about equal to the outside atmospheric pressure.

During the next ninety degrees of crank rotation shown in Fig. 4, the displacer is rapidly moving from the cold side to the hot side. This transfers the air back around the displacer to the cold side. The transferred warm air loses thermal energy to the cold plate, and drops its temperature. The pressure within the engine drops also because the volume of the engine air is virtually constant since the piston is rounding its outer dead center. Again, energy stored in the rotating flywheel carries out this "transfer" stroke too.

Since the air was just about equal to atmospheric pressure before the last transfer stroke, it ends up being below atmospheric pressure afterward. Thus during the last quarter revolution shown in Fig. 5, atmospheric pressure pushes the piston inward. Although the entire inward stroke is called the "compression" because the piston moves inward and decreases the volume of the engine air, it also contributes work to the engine shaft as long as the pressure inside is below the outside pressure. During this last part of the cycle the displacer remains close to the hot plate and the heat of compression is dissipated out through the cold plate of the engine.

The Stirling Cycle

These four processes constitute the operating cycle of every Stirling engine: heating at constant volume, expansion, cooling at constant volume, and compression. In most simple Stirling engines, the pressure fluctuates above and below the external atmospheric pressure and so both the expansion and the compression strokes deliver some work to the crankshaft. The momentum of the flywheel carries the engine over the rest of the operating cycle.

The Stirling engine operates on what is called a "closed" cycle. There is no intake or exhaust and the engine uses the same air over and over transferring it back and forth between the hot and the cold sides and letting the resulting pressure changes push and pull the piston. Since the Stirling is a closed cycle engine, it really doesn't care what its "heat source" and "heat sink" are as long as the temperature difference is enough to overcome the internal friction of the engine. It just takes in thermal energy from whatever warms its hot side and rejects heat to whatever keeps its cold side cool, which is usually the surrounding air.

It is this availability of a heat source and a heat sink at different temperatures that drives the Stirling cycle, and indeed all engine cycles.[1] As we have seen in the case of the Stirling engine, temperature difference is responsible for creating the change in pressure within the engine, and it also induces heat flow into and out of

---

[1] The Second Law of Thermodynamics requires a temperature differential for all engine cycles.

the engine. Moreover, the difference between the heat flow in and the heat flow out is exactly the net work of the engine each cycle.[1]

Hot water is an excellent heat source for demonstrating LTD Stirling engines. A very convenient configuration is that first used by the author on the Argonne Stirling which was designed so that the engine could be placed on top of a container of water. With a well-insulated container, a LTD engine can run for hours. As an extreme example, the P-19 engine once ran nine hours over a few cups of hot water in a thick-walled styrofoam basin.

Actually, the roles of the upper and lower plates can be reversed in LTD engines, that is, the top plate can be made to function as the hot and the lower as the cold. This changes the phasing of the displacer by 180° so the engine will operate in the opposite direction.[2] A LTD engine can run in this regime for example when placed on top of an object colder than the surrounding air. The air is then the heat source and the cold object is the heat sink, at least as long as it stays cold. A LTD engine placed on top of a dish of ice water can run for a long time because of the relatively large quantity of heat that ice absorbs in melting[3]. For example, an engine manufactured by New Machine Company will run for about 6 hours if just 6 ice cubes are initially put in its insulated base.

Anywhere there is a difference in temperatures there is a theoretical opportunity to operate an engine. Thermodynamicists have long known this well. With the technology of LTD Stirling engines available, we can now actually take advantage of many opportunities with really small temperature differences. Properly designed and well built Stirling engines can operate at very small temperature differences indeed.

---

[1] This statement is a form of the First Law of Thermodynamics applicable to all engine cycles.

[2] This is because the criterion that the displacer reaches its cold plate dead center 90° before the piston reaches its outer dead center piston is fulfilled in this direction. Note that the Ringbom engine is an exception to this.

[3] called the "heat of fusion".

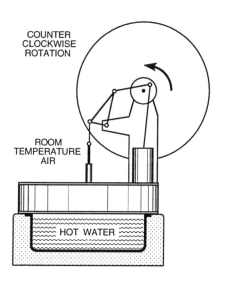

COUNTER
CLOCKWISE
ROTATION

ROOM
TEMPERATURE
AIR

HOT WATER

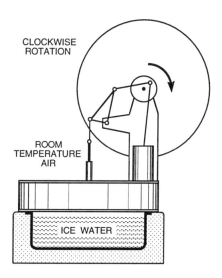

CLOCKWISE
ROTATION

ROOM
TEMPERATURE
AIR

ICE WATER

Reversing the temperature difference between the engine plates reverses the direction of rotation of the engine.

The Geometry of LTD Stirling Engines

What makes a LTD Stirling engine different from a conventional flame-heated or high temperature differential engine is simply the size and shape of the displacer unit. LTD engines favor a short displacer with a large area and having a short stroke. The reasons for this come from the basic physics underlying all heat engines.

There is a definite relationship between the compression ratio of an engine and the temperatures between which it can operate. Although experiments and trial and error hinted at the qualitative character of this connection, the exact and explicit mathematical relationship was not discovered until 1985 .[1] This relationship dictates that *engines operating at low temperature differentials must have low compression ratios*. It is an inescapable consequence of the laws of physics governing the wonderful world we were given. Thus we know for sure now that we are not making LTD engines with low compression ratios just because the first one happened to be made that way and it worked. The fact is that it simply cannot be done any other way.

Now given that the compression ratio must be low if the temperature differential is low, this implies that the volume swept out by the displacer must be relatively large compared to that of the piston for a LTD Stirling engine. For a LTD Stirling engine to run satisfactorily on the heat of a hand, its displacer must sweep out a volume about 50 times that of the piston. The displacer swept volume equals the displacer stroke times its area, and the area is proportional to the *square* of the diameter. Hence the best way to get a large volume out of reasonable size is with a large diameter and short stroke.

The additional role of the displacer in any Stirling engine is as an insulator between the hot and cold sides of the engine. The displacer must thermally isolate the hot air section from the cold section. Since heat conduction through the displacer represents a loss

---

[1] For more information on this particular topic, study the technical papers under the heading *Mechanical Efficiency* in the list of References.

in efficiency of the engine, the displacer must limit this kind of heat flow. The rate of heat conduction through a solid is directly proportional to the temperature difference at each end and inversely proportional to its length. Therefore a LTD engine does not require a long displacer to keep conduction losses down to a reasonable level. Moreover, styrofoam is an excellent material for making displacers in LTD engines and a very short displacer made from this material will suffice. Hence short displacers are favored for LTD engines. This is also consistent with a short stroke.

The physics of heat transfer also favors a large diameter displacer for LTD engines, in fact, the larger, the better. Consider an engine with a displacer chamber that is large enough to allow the engine to run. This means the four step cycle that was described above is being repeatedly carried out within the engine. This includes the heat flow from the hot plate to the engine air, and then later in the cycle from the engine air to the cold plate. The rate of heat transfer between the surface of the plate and the engine air next to it is directly proportional to the area of the plate and to the temperature difference between the plate and the air. If the plate were to be made larger in diameter, the active area would be greater so the rate of heat transfer would increase. This would allow the engine to run faster than before.

Therefore, from the point of view of heat transfer, the larger the plate diameter, the better. But there is an important practical consideration that prevents us from making really huge round displacers with ultra tiny strokes. This is the difficulty of keeping a large diameter displacer flat enough and square enough to its rod to permit the displacer to come up close against the plates. The larger the displacer, the closer it must approach the plates to limit the dead space .[1] From the above discussion, it should be clear now why LTD engines have the shape they do, and more generally, how the geometry of any Stirling engine matches the temperature differential that it can best work between.

---

[1] With a large diameter displacer, a little bit of end-stroke clearance introduces a lot of dead volume.

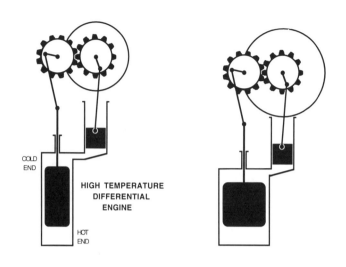

HIGH TEMPERATURE
DIFFERENTIAL
ENGINE

COLD
END

HOT
END

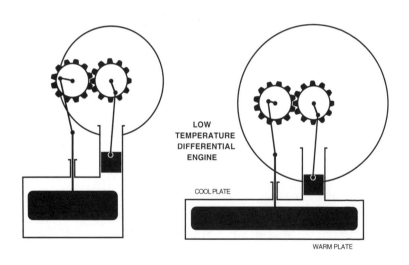

LOW
TEMPERATURE
DIFFERENTIAL
ENGINE

COOL PLATE

WARM PLATE

The geometry of a Stirling engine corresponds to the temperatures between which it operates optimally.

Running LTD Stirling Engines

Successful operation of a LTD Stirling engine requires that a temperature difference be established and maintained between the engine plates, that the geometry be right for that temperature difference, and that everything else be in proper working order. So long as these conditions are met, the engine will function caring so to speak neither where the heat is coming from nor where it is going outside of itself. All that matters to the engine is that the heat source and heat sink are capable of maintaining the temperature differential between its plates as it runs.

Usually the heat sink is the atmospheric or room air. In this setting, a heat source is required with a temperature above that of the surrounding air. The plate to which the engine delivers its reject thermal energy during its cycle thereby warms up and so heat flows from the plate out to and is carried away by atmospheric air. For LTD Stirling engines there is an abundance of adequate heat sources above ambient temperature: a cup of warm water, the top of a television set,[1] or even the heat of a human hand.

An adequate temperature differential can also be established by cooling the top plate. Here the atmospheric air becomes the heat source and the cold object the heat sink. An ice cold drink simply placed on top is enough to run some sensitive LTD engines, like the P-19 or N-92 engines. P-19 has also been operated on the cooling effect of evaporating water. The engine was set up with two cloth pads covering most of its top plate. The pads were kept moistened by wicks which fed water from two cups on the table beside the engine. The engine was set up on small blocks so that air could naturally circulate under the bottom plate. Evaporation of the water from the cloth pads kept the engine top plate between 3° and 4°F cooler than the bottom plate. On this temperature difference the engine ran non-stop for 16 days. During this marathon, the cups had to be topped off with water

---

[1] This is an excellent educational use of TV, especially if it's tuned to a station with no program on.

about every other day. The engine was finally stopped because it was needed by a student at the university for a seminar demonstration.

As mentioned already, most LTD engines can run with the temperature differential across the plates reversed, that is, with the upper plate warmer than the lower plate. This can be established by cooling the lower plate below ambient temperature or by warming the top plate above ambient temperature (or both). For a small LTD engine, there are many ways to do this.   Just placing some LTD engines out on a sunny day provides sufficient warmth. It helps if the top plate is painted black for this kind of operation. Indoors in the wintertime, it is easy to find a cold windowsill that a LTD engine can run on; if the sun is shining in too, so much the better! Also as mentioned before, placing an engine over ice is a good way to get long runs.

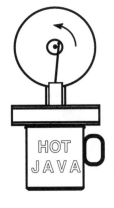

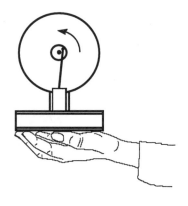

43

The Performance of LTD Engines

As fascinating and as instructional as LTD Stirling engines are, they are not big power producers. Common sense alone dictates that an engine which runs on the warmth of a human hand cannot produce as much as an engine being heated by a blowtorch. This, and the reasons behind it, have to be realized and understood well in order to design, construct, and apply LTD engines intelligently.

Slow speed operation is an intrinsic characteristic of LTD engines. To understand clearly why this is so, consider the problem of heating and cooling the air within the engine to make it perform its cycle. As already discussed, the displacer causes this to happen by moving the air back and forth between the hot and the cold sections of the engine. When cold air enters the hot section, it picks up heat from the hot engine surfaces and so rises in temperature. When the warm air is later moved back into the cooler section, it loses thermal energy to the cooler engine surfaces and drops in temperature. It is this cyclic change in the temperature of the working air that causes its pressure to change and drives the piston to run the whole machine and do useful work.

The heat transfer between the engine surfaces and the air inside is caused by the temperature difference between them. In more precise terms, as already noted above, the rate of heat transfer is directly proportional to the difference in their temperatures. In order to get thermal energy from one to the other, one has to be hotter or warmer than the other, and the higher the difference in temperature the proportionally faster does the transfer of thermal energy take place. In conventional Stirling or hot air engines, the walls of the hot section are very hot, often red hot, and so the transfer of thermal energy to air entering the hot section is rapid. Similarly, very hot air entering the cooler section rapidly drops in temperature. That is why flame heated Stirling engines can run so surprisingly fast. Likewise, the smaller the temperature difference between the engine air and the surface of the material which it is near, the longer the heat transfer will take. This is why LTD engines tend to be low speed machines.

Also, because in a LTD engine the temperature change of the engine air is small, the resulting pressure change over the cycle is correspondingly low. This means that the work produced over a cycle is lower in a LTD engine than in a high temperature differential engine.

Finally, the thermal efficiency of a LTD engine is inherently limited. The thermal efficiency of an engine is the work that it delivers to the piston in a cycle divided by the heat that it takes in. It is the measure of how good the engine is at converting heat into raw mechanical energy. The highest thermal efficiency that any engine cycle can have is the well-known Carnot efficiency[1] which is the engine's temperature differential divided by its absolute upper temperature. In symbols,

$$\text{Carnot Thermal Efficiency} \ = \ \frac{T_H - T_C}{T_H}$$

where T_H and T_C are the temperatures of the hot and cold sides of the engine expressed on an absolute scale such as the Kelvin.[2] In an LTD engine the temperature differential is low. This means the numerator of the Carnot efficiency fraction is small compared to the denominator. Hence the thermal efficiency of LTD engines is intrinsically low.

It is enlightening to calculate how low this can be. Consider running a LTD engine on the heat of a hand, such as the N-92 engine to be described in the second part of this book. Standard room temperature is about 20°C and normal human body temperature is 37°C. Therefore the difference between T_H and T_C is 17°K while T_H is 37 + 273 = 310°K on the Kelvin absolute temperature scale. The Carnot efficiency thus turns out to be

---

[1] Carnot efficiency is also described on pages 13-16 of *An Introduction to Stirling Engines*

[2] The Kelvin scale has the same size degree as the Celsius, but starts at "absolute zero". Kelvin scale temperature equals the Celsius temperature plus 273. Note that because the degree size is the same, a temperature *differential* is the same in either the Celsius or the Kelvin scale.

$$\frac{T_H - T_C}{T_H} = \frac{17}{310} = .0548...$$

Hence the absolute best efficiency you can hope to get from an engine running on your hand is less than five and one-half percent. This means under 5.5% of the heat being absorbed from your hand can converted into mechanical energy.

And this is a really optimistic estimate ! First of all, hands are usually cooler than 37°C. Then there is the fact that the engine hot plate will be a little cooler than your hand because the engine in running is taking the thermal energy it needs each cycle from the plate and so is cooling it. Next, the cold plate will be warmer than the room air because the engine is delivering its reject heat to it and so is warming it. In practice we have found that typically a LTD engine running on a human hand achieves a steady state temperature difference of only about 6°C (11°F) . This would put the Carnot efficiency limit of a hand-heated LTD engine way down to around 2%.

And that too is optimistic ! An engine can only attain the maximal Carnot efficiency if it is perfect, and of course nothing in this world is. Engines rarely reach half of their Carnot efficiency potential because of such things as irreversible heat transfer losses, internal flow losses, heat leaks, and conduction paths. So we're down to about 1% efficiency at this point. But this is only the *thermal* efficiency. The overall efficiency of an engine is even lower because of non-thermal losses due to friction in the engine mechanism and air leakage.

With all this in mind, it is truly amazing that LTD Stirling engines can run at all on a few degrees of temperature differential. Although a well built LTD Stirling may appear to be running with ease when held in your hand, it is really against pretty strong odds. Everything in the engine has to be just right.

Of course, if an engine balks, you can always up the temperature differential. With boiling hot water against one plate and ice water on the other, the odds are much better. In this case the Carnot efficiency limit would be

$$\frac{T_H - T_C}{T_H} = \frac{100}{373} = .268...$$

or almost 27%. This gives the engine a much better chance, even with all the losses due to imperfections taken off. In addition to this efficiency advantage when a larger temperature differential is used, the compression ratio can also be increased for more power. As mentioned earlier, there is a correlation between the temperatures that an engine can work at and its compression ratio. The technical papers listed under the heading *Mechanical Efficiency* in the references section at the end of the book provide all the mathematical details. In general practical terms, the larger the temperature differential, the larger the compression ratio can be and the greater the power the engine is capable of producing.

The lesson to be had from these elementary thermodynamic calculations is that everything is more critical the lower the temperature differential is. This is important to keep in mind when operating, repairing, designing, or constructing LTD Stirling engines.

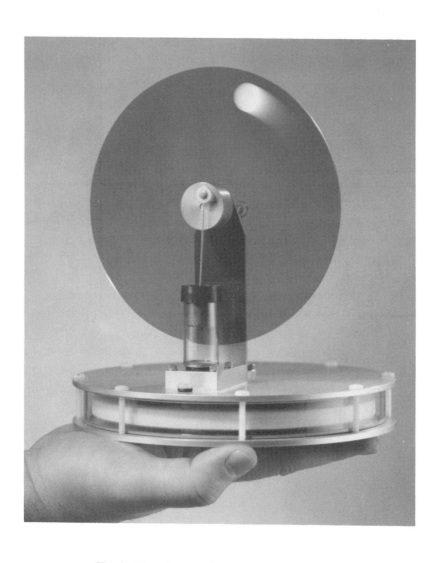

The N-92 engine running on the heat of a hand.
(Photo by NASA - Lewis Research Center)

III. Construction

How to Make "N-92", a Stirling Engine That Will Run on Your Hand

N-92 is a Stirling engine that was specifically designed for hand held operation. It was proportioned to operate as well as any engine possibly could at the temperature differential typically produced and maintained in a hand held engine. At the same time, it is of substantial construction and not too delicate to be enjoyed running on a wide variety of heat sources. Virtually all of the modes of operating LTD engines described earlier in this book can be used to run N-92.

The prototype begins operating when there is a temperature difference of just over 3°F (1.8°C) across its plates. Its geometry was selected to be optimal for a temperature differential of around 11°F (6°C), which is the usual steady state operating temperature difference when hand held. Its free speed when under these conditions is about 175 rpm. At larger temperature differences it runs faster of course.

N-92 requires the use of a lathe and drill press for its construction. While LTD engines can be made with hand tools alone, the process is much more certain and the performance more reliable when precision can be built into the engine component by component. On the other hand, N-92 does not require an unusually high degree of machining skill to work well. What it requires most of all is to be made with care and patience. LTD engines do not tolerate leakage and friction well at all. The piston must be the finest of airtight but totally free and smooth fits in its cylinder and the mechanism must not exhibit even the slightest tendency to bind or stick.

If you have already built your own conventional flame-heated hot air engine then you know something about how important low friction and low leakage are to those engines. It's just even more important for LTD Stirling engines. The smaller the temperature difference, the better built it has to be.

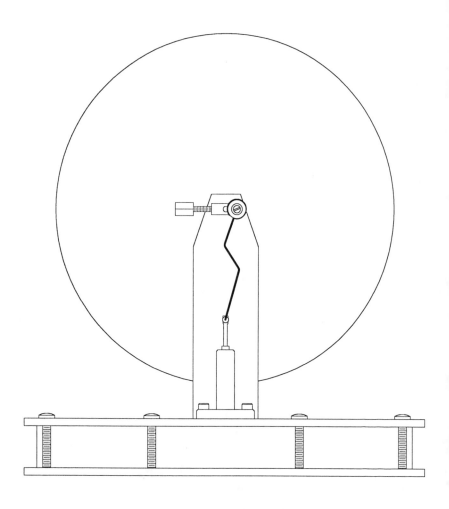

A view of the the N-92 showing the displacer drive.

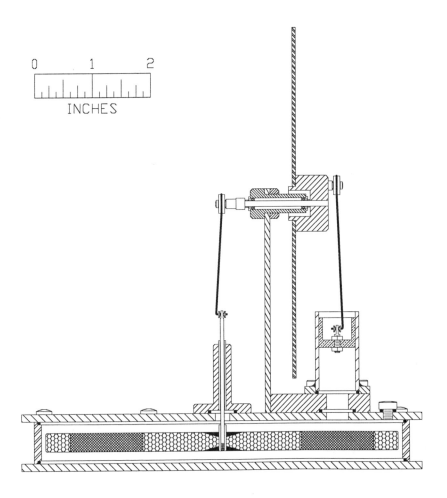

INCHES

A sectional view of the N-92 engine.

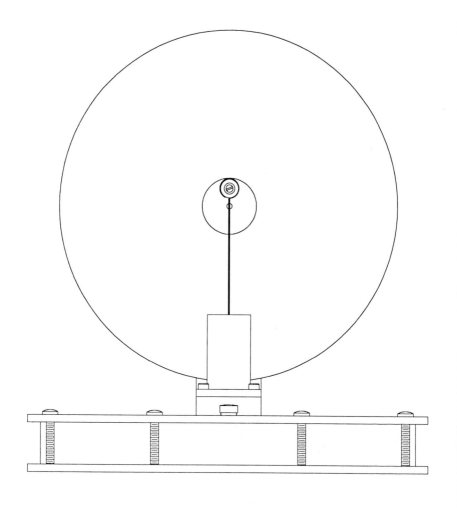

A view of the N-92 from the cylinder side.

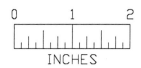

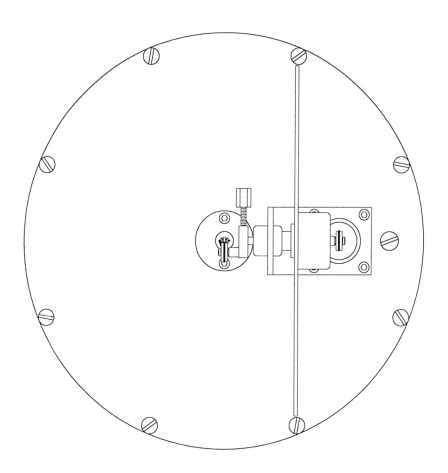

The top view of the N-92 engine.

Displacer Chamber Ring

The displacer chamber ring on the first N-92 was cut from a left over piece of tubing obtained from a local plastics supply house. If you cannot find the same size tubing, the ring can be machined from solid acrylic plate. The author has done this for a number of LTD engines. In this case, a square of 3/4" thick acrylic can be mounted on the faceplate by four bolts in the corners. Spacing the material away for the faceplate is a good idea here to save the equipment! A center disc can then be trepanned out (don't worry about wasting plastic, this disc will come in handy for all sorts of other projects as you will see) and the hole finished to 6.25" ID with a boring tool. Next, on the bandsaw, the ring can be rough sawn out. Machine a wooden disc mounted to the faceplate to serve as a mandrel for the rest of the machining on the ring. Turn the mandrel so the ring is a good push fit on it; this is enough to drive the material for finishing the OD if light cuts are taken with a properly sharpened tool. Take out tool marks with fine wet or dry paper and buff the ring to a clear surface so that you'll be able to watch the displacer moving inside when the engine is running.

If you find tubing from which to make your ring, you'll notice that it is not as round as if you had machined it yourself from solid material. Commercial tolerances on tubing this big are surprisingly large. But don't worry since there is over 1/16" radial clearance between the displacer and the ring so some out-of-roundness can be tolerated.

Whether you got your ring the easy or the hard way, it can now be faced to length on the mandrel already described. The length should turn out no less than .703", and if it is .010 or .015" longer, it will be just fine. The O-ring grooves can be machined at this point also. Actually, because of the thin wall of the ring, they are not full grooves but just steps. The angle to the step is there to encourage the ring to stay in place as the engine is assembled. Try to get the depth that is specified close so that the O-ring will stand sufficiently proud of the ring to be able to seal against the plates. For this operation, a nice sharp tool is necessary to get a smooth finish on the bottom surface of the O-ring step; a rough finish here may prevent the O-ring from sealing. During this operation, a band clamp can be put around the ring to hold it more securely on the mandrel if you're worried that yours is too loose. Mine was tight, but I still stuck tape from the ring to the faceplate for more security.

The O-rings are made by gluing up cord stock. Use nominal 1/16" (actual size is about .070" dia.) cord stock in as soft a durometer as you can find. Local bearing and hydraulic supply houses as well as mail order machinist suppliers carry O-ring stock. I used the silicone variety, cut the ends square, and glued them together with instant glue.

Hot and Cold Plates

Both engine heat exchanger plates are made form 1/8" thick aluminum. You may want to specifically use alloy 6061 for the plates so that you can have them anodized to prevent corrosion and discoloration that comes with long and hard usage. Some of my engines which were not anodized developed a "patina" which although slightly tarnished looking, is not too bad and which seems to resist further discoloration. However, other engine plates have corroded badly when left in contact with water for a time. If you're not going to anodize, you may want to eventually coat the bottom plate with a hot water resistant finish.

In any case, you'll want to start with pieces that are flat and smooth. Distortion and deep scratches may prevent the O-rings from sealing. On some engines, I have taken a light facing cut over the plates to take out slight imperfections. For this operation, the plates were stuck with double-sided tape to the lathe faceplate. This holds just fine if everything is clean and generous pieces of tape are used. The main problem is getting them unstuck when the cut is finished! Gentle heating helps to unstick most tapes. If you decide to surface machine the plates for your engine, you'll probably want to do it as the last operation after all the other work on the plates is finished.

When locating the holes in the top plate, keep in mind that only the eight outer screws center the ring in the final assembly. Thus these holes should be located carefully with respect to the center hole so that the displacer will move free and clear of the ring. If the displacer rubs the ring, the friction will easily prevent the engine from operating. The radius shown on the drawing allows .010" clearance between the screws and the outside of the ring; you can measure your ring carefully and locate the holes for less clearance if desired. The eight corresponding holes in the bottom plate should match those in the top plate of course. The two can be clamped and drilled together, but only tapping size; then the top plate holes can be opened out to clearance size. The bottom plate could be secured using nuts rather than tapped holes, but nuts will prevent good thermal contact when you will want to set the engine down on a flat heat source or sink like the top of the TV or on a cold windowsill. Tapping these holes is worth the few minutes of extra work.

There are six 4-40 tapped holes in the top plate. Four of these are for mounting the base block and two for the displacer rod gland. The single 8-32 tapped hole is merely a vent hole which is normally plugged with a screw and O-ring or gasket washer. Its purpose is to have a way of releasing the compression of the engine so that the free movement and balance of the engine can be established after assembly.

Displacer and Rod

The displacer is basically a disc of styrofoam. The blue or pink varieties are recommended over the white kind since they are more stable. On the P-19 engine, I used a piece of white styrofoam that was packing material originally. After some use - considerable use actually - it warped slightly and began hitting the plates, which took extra energy and slowed the engine down. On N-92, blue was used and has held up well. A hot wire cutter was used to slice some slabs to the desired thickness. A piece of nichrome wire was stretched above a flat board and warmed up by low voltage from a train transformer.

Styrofoam slabs were then slid on the board into the wire. The material should come out no thicker than 5/16" and no thinner than 9/32". I use only the center sections, that is, pieces that I wire cut on both sides since it was noticed that pieces that have the original factory surface on one side tend to warp in time.

Before cutting the disc from the sliced displacer material, the center bushing should be made and mounted as shown in the detail drawing. The bushing is 1/8" dia aluminum (or brass) reamed 1/16" dia to fit the displacer rod closely with some 0-80 thread at the end to secure it. At this point, you will have to make the rod or at least thread the end of it as shown in its drawing. It is needed to fixture the bushing in the displacer.

A crater is cut or heat-formed around a central hole in the displacer stock. The bushing is then positioned in it and glued in with epoxy. The epoxy when set forms a washer-like bearing on the foam. This spreads the load over enough area to hold up to fast running. To fixture the bushing, a vee block can be used to hold the displacer rod exactly perpendicular to the displacer, which is very important. Waxed paper beneath the displacer will prevent it from bonding to the workbench! Be careful to keep glue off the rod so it will unscrew after the glue sets. I put a little dot of tape on the bottom of the bushing to keep glue form creeping up into the threads. When set, the rod can be unscrewed and the displacer outline can be scribed from the now firmly established center, rough cut, and then finished on a disc sander.

Next the six holes for the regenerator elements can be cut. I used a piece of sharpened thin wall tubing cookie-cutter style to make these holes. Into these holes are glued polyurethane or polyester filter foam discs which serve as the regenerator. Filter foam of the kind used for air conditioners is ideal and can be purchased at the local hardware store. You'll need foam that has a fine but open structure and that is about 1/4" thick. The kind I used on N-92 (and P-19) is made by American Air Filter Co. of Louisville Kentucky. It is a very fine material but as purchased was of non-uniform thickness ranging between 3/8" and 1/2" thick. The material was compressed between two plates spaced 1/4" apart, put in a 280°F oven, baked for 15 minutes, and then allowed to cool still between the plates. After this treatment, the material came out beautifully flat and exactly 1/4" thick. When glued in place in the displacer body, the regenerator discs should be flush with the styrofoam surface or just slightly below.

Alternately, the regenerator elements can be made square. Matching square holes can be cut in the displacer disc with a razor knife. To get the same amount of regenerator, each of the six elements should be about 1 1/8 X 1 1/8".

It is not at all necessary to put in the regenerator windows; the engine will run without them. But the engine will run considerably faster with the regenerators. You may want to make a plain displacer at first and then later make a regenerative one and see the improvement first hand. If you go with a plain displacer, make it about 3/16" smaller in diameter to make it easier for the air to flow around the displacer. Adding six 1/2" dia holes through the displacer spaced like the regenerators will also make it easier for the displacer to pull away from near the plates.

The displacer rod can now be finished by flattening the end and crossdrilling a .035" hole for the connecting rod. The flattening operation in my case was carried out by squeezing the rod end in the milling machine vise between two pieces of hardened steel.

Displacer Gland

The body of the displacer rod gland is turned from aluminum bar stock. After roughing the outer shape and cutting off from the bar, rechuck and face, drill, and counterbore for the O-ring. You can find a suitable O-ring for this part at the local hardware store. After drilling the two holes in the flange for mounting, loctite a length of 1/16" ID brass tubing in the gland body. The brass will wear well with just a little dry graphite as lubricant, whereas soft steel running dry in aluminum tends to gall. Be sure to select your rod and tubing combination to be a close running fit. There should be not more than

.001" diametrical difference between the two. More clearance means unnecessary leakage and performance will suffer.

Displacer Section Assembly

At this point, the displacer section can be assembled and checked. Fasten the displacer gland to the top plate with two 4-40 screws. Don't forget the O-ring! Some thread sealant should be put on the screws before assembly so there is no leakage along the threads. The displacer rod is passed thought the gland and screwed into the displacer. Check at this point that the displacer is truly parallel to the plate so that it approaches the plate squarely. If it is far off, then when the engine is completely assembled, it will hit the plates instead of just getting up close and this will cause binding and diminish performance or altogether prevent it from running.

The two plates can now be assembled with the displacer chamber ring in between. Again, don't forget the O-rings! Conduction between the plates can be minimized by using Nylon screws. They are plenty strong enough because if the plates are reasonably flat and the O-rings grooves smooth, not much force is needed to seal the O-rings. If you cannot get (or make) Nylon screws, then stainless steel is the next best. The screws should be cut to be flush with the bottom plate when they are tight.

With assembly complete, check that the displacer moves freely inside the chamber. It should not make contact with the plastic ring and its rod should be free sliding in the gland. Measure the free travel of the displacer and to make sure it is a little more than 3/8". The original N-92 has a free travel of .42". If you have a lot more free travel, you can make the displacer crank throw a little larger than the drawing to compensate. If the free travel of the displacer is short, then check that the displacer is square to the rod so that it can approach the plates closely. If out of square, it should be corrected by removing and regluing the displacer rod bushing. The object when the engine is finished is to have a displacer stroke of about 3/8" with the displacer coming close to but not touching either plate.

Cylinder and Piston

The fit between the cylinder and its piston is crucial to the performance of any LTD engine. The smaller the temperature differential that you want your engine to run on, the better the fit will have to be. To run on a hand, not only must the piston leakage be minuscule, but so must be the friction. Furthermore, the piston must run dry in the cylinder. Although oil improves the sealing of a piston in its cylinder, it introduces too much viscous drag for very low temperature differential operation. Thus in addition to an airtight smooth free fit, the piston and cylinder materials must be compatible for dry running.

The best material found thus far for a piston in these engines is graphite. It is self-lubricating of course and easy to precisely machine to an extremely close fit in a smooth true cylinder. Moreover, the loading on the piston is very low in LTD engines and so graphite pistons last a long time. Indeed, graphite pistons seem to work very well in high temperature difference engines as well. Several of the author's flame heated engines including the 10" fan Moriya have logged many hours running with graphite pistons in metal cylinders. Solid graphite is readily obtainable in bar form from large industrial, EDM, and laboratory supply houses.

The cylinder must be smooth and true to a high degree of precision. Honing or lapping is essential. Brass is the material specified in the drawing, but bronze or stainless steel will work fine also. Indeed, so would steel but for the rusting problem. You may wish to make the wall thicker than called for in the drawing for more rigidity while machining. The cylinder specified in the drawing is fabricated by attaching a flange to the cylinder barrel with solder or epoxy. Following this, the flange can be faced true and the recess for the O-ring machined. Machining the cylinder from solid square (or round) stock is also an alternative. You can omit the O-ring groove if you instead use a gasket, but make sure that it seals perfectly. The cylinder can be made longer than specified in the drawing. This is a good idea actually because you will be able to experiment with longer strokes when running the engine at larger temperature differences. Also, the piston could be made longer for a better seal.[1]

Honing or lapping the inside to a smooth true finish should be left as the final operation on the cylinder. The degree of precision required in the cylinder of a successful LTD engine cannot be overemphasized. A local machine shop should be able to satisfactorily hone the cylinder for you, but lapping is an alternative that can be done in the home shop.[2] The finish does not have to be glass smooth, but should approach this as close as possible. The smoother the finish, the longer the piston will last. Having the bore hard chrome plated before honing or lapping will allow a better finish to be obtained and give longer life.

Once the cylinder is finished, the piston can be turned to fit. In the final stages, I use the old trick of setting the lathe topslide over to an angle of just under 6 degrees.[3] Then every thousandth of topslide feed moves the tool inward just one tenth. This allows very fine cuts to be taken if the lathe is in good condition and the tool is sharp. Graphite is so soft that this method works extremely well to get a close fit of the piston to its cylinder. Aim for the closest fit[4] you can get without any tightness or drag.

An alternative to making your own piston and cylinder is to order a cylinder unit from the Airpot Corporation. This company makes exquisitely fitted Pyrex glass cylinder and graphite piston units for commercial use as dashpots. They are ideal for LTD Stirling engines. Perhaps the best testimony to this is that an Airpot cylinder was used on the record setting P-19 engine. N-92 used one as well as can be seen in the photographs. If you decide to use an Airpot, you won't have to worry about that part of the engine being good enough!

---

[1] The rate of leakage past a close clearance piston is inversely proportional to the length of the piston.

[2] Articles dealing with the subject of lapping cylinders are listed in the References section at the end of the book.

[3] The exact angle is $\arcsin(.1) = 5.739...°$

[4] The closeness of the fit is extremely critical because the rate of leakage past a plain piston is also proportional to the *cube* of the clearance.

After seeing some LTD engines equipped with Airpot cylinders that I brought along on lecture trips to the Australian National University, model engineers Michael Shelley and Trevor Dowling made a number of interesting LTD engines including Ringbom types which featured their own glass cylinders "homemade" from laboratory glass tubing. As supplied, this tubing is nowhere near round and straight enough to take a piston, so a nice thick wall variety was chosen and the bore lapped true. Their expanding laps were made from rigid PVC pipe rather than the usual copper or other soft metal. Silicon carbide 220 grit was used to first rough lap the inside to a true cylinder. Then successively finer grades were used to take out the scratches left by the previous grit finishing with 1000 grit. Thorough cleaning is essential when changing to a finer grit, and in fact changing to new laps is best. The final polishing was done with a new lap and cerium oxide powder to obtain a "glass smooth" finish. I have seen some of the cylinder and piston units that these gentlemen have made and they are indeed perfect fits. They recommend starting with a longer piece of tube than needed and then after the lapping is finished, cutting about 1/2" off each end. This eliminates the "bellmouth" problem and is good advice even when making metal cylinders. Mike actually uses a length sufficient for two or three cylinders at a time and then cuts them apart.[1] If you plan to try making glass cylinders, wear protective gloves!

Another possibility is to use a diaphragm instead of a piston. As pointed out earlier, this is what Prof. Kolin uses exclusively on his engines. There is plenty of room on N-92 to incorporate a diaphragm if a slightly smaller diameter flywheel is used. A diaphragm of 1-1/2" diameter and 5/16" stroke would theoretically give the same swept volume as the cylinder/piston unit specified, but either of these dimensions may have to be increased to compensate for "ballooning"

---

[1] Glass tubing can be most easily cut with a thin diamond cutoff wheel. Both Mike and I have also cut glass tubing by holding a thin brass strip against slowly rotating tubing with abrasive slurry applied; this is a slow but sure process.

of the diaphragm. Keep in mind that although diaphragms do not leak, they do suffer internal friction, so very thin flexible rubber should be used.

Piston Yoke

The piston yoke is the part that joins the piston to the connecting rod yet to be made. It can be made by filing a flat on the end of a 4-40 screw and then cross drilling it .035" A nut is fitted and the threads sealed with loctite, glue, or solder. It is mounted in the piston with a thin washer cut from gasket material and a nut on the outside as shown on the assembly drawing. A finished graphite piston should be handled with care to keep it clean and oil free. Use a piece of tissue or a piece of paper towel when handling the piston. Don't tighten the nut too tight to avoid cracking the piston!

Base Block

If you make the base block next, you'll be able to give the engine a bit of a tryout. The base block forms the mount for the cylinder and the upright bearing plate which holds the main shaft bearings. It is straightforward machining. The O-ring groove on the bottom can be cut by mounting the block in the 4-jaw chuck. If you are using an Airpot cylinder, then you'll want to tap the big hole 3/8-32 so that the Airpot cylinder head can screw directly into it. Use an O-ring about 3/4" OD to seal the Airpot cylinder head against the block.

At this point the block and cylinder can be assembled onto the displacer chamber with 4-40 machine screws. Cut the screws to length so that they do not protrude through the top plate. Put sealer on the ends to prevent air leakage along the threads.

You can make up a temporary wire connecting rod at this time so that the piston can be pushed back and forth in its cylinder. Find a short 8-32 screw and O-ring to seal up the compression release hole in the top plate. You should feel a "springiness" or "bounce" to the piston if it is pushed or pulled and released. Let free, it should take several minutes to imperceptibly sink to the bottom of the cylinder. If it falls faster, there is a leak somewhere that must be tracked down and fixed.

If all is well so far, you can now warm the lower plate and cycle the displacer by hand. The piston should respond by moving up and down as the pressure in the engine changes. If you engine behaves in this way, it will run fine.

Bearing Plate, Housing, and Collar

The bearing plate is cut from 3/32" thick aluminum sheet. The two holes at the bottom for mounting to the base block can be countersunk as shown if desired for flathead 5-40 screws.

The bearing housing is machined from 1/2" round bar stock and reamed through 3/16" dia. for the ball bearings. These bearings are flanged and do not need to be a press fit into the housing. The ID of the bearings is 3/32". Two sources for miniature ball bearings are listed at the end of the book. If you cannot get flanged bearings, plain ball bearings will work as well, but then you will have to machine the bearing housing with suitable counterbores or use a sleeve. Get shielded bearings if possible to help prevent dust from entering and increasing friction. If the bearings come grease lubricated, remove it with solvent and lubricate lightly with watch or clock oil.

The bearing collar is a slip fit over the bearing housing and is loctited to it up against the bearing plate. This makes a neater and more secure assembly rather than gluing just the bearing housing into the plate.

Flywheel, Hub, Crankshaft, and Crankpins

The flywheel hub is turned from aluminum bar stock. The deep counterbore brings the flywheel mass between the two main bearings, which minimizes the friction loss due to gravity. The center is reamed 3/32" dia. for a close fit on the main shaft. The flywheel disc mounts on the step of the hub which should be turned at the same chucking to minimize wobble of the flywheel. Carefully locate and drill and tap the 0-80 hole in the hub for the crankpin retaining screw. Also drill and tap radially to take a 2-56 screw for securing the hub to the engine shaft. A brass fillister head screw is ideal for this. The flywheel is a disc cut from 1/16" thick plastic sheet and glued to the hub.

The crankshaft is a piece of 3/32" dia. rod that is nice and straight and slips easily into the inner bore of the bearings. You may have to reduce the diameter of the rod you have on hand by polishing in the lathe or drill press with emery paper. As you work, carefully wipe off the rod and your fingers before picking up the bearings to try the fit. When you get a nice slip fit, make the rectangular throw piece from steel, brass, or aluminum. Loctite the two together if they are not a press fit. Check that the outer face of the throw is square to the shaft axis; if it looks crooked, chuck the shaft and take a light facing cut across it in the lathe. Drill and tap the 0-80 hole for the crankpin. The specified offset is 3/16" to give a stroke of 3/8" to the displacer. Now if your displacer came out a bit too thick or if your ring turned out a little shorter, you can decrease the stroke somewhat to compensate. Even if you decrease it 1/16" the engine will still run on your hand if everything else is OK - I tried it on my N-92. When figuring the stroke, remember to allow for .020 to .030" clearance between the displacer and each plate.

The 2-56 tapped hole in the crankthrow that is shown in the drawing is for fitting a balance weight for the displacer. It can be seen in the photos and the assembly drawings. A length of 2-56 screw goes into this hole and carries a short length of threaded brass hex rod as the weight. By screwing the weight closer in or farther out, the weight of the displacer can be exactly statically balanced. This is done with the flywheel off after the displacer connecting rod is made and fitted in place. The balance weight is not essential. The engine will start up sooner and run at a lower temperature differential with it, but it will still run on your hand without it; you'll just have to warm it up a bit longer before turning over the flywheel.

Now turn the tiny crankpins. Steel is specified but brass, aluminum or even delrin can be used. Turn the 3/32" dia. portion about .001" smaller than the bearing ID; a little bit of freedom here will avoid slight misalignment problems. The bearings used here on the connecting rods are the same size as used on the main shaft but are unflanged.[1] Note the angle to the step on the crankpin drawings. The angle is not critical but is an important feature. It insures that the crankpin will only engage the inner race of the bearing and clear the rest of it. At this point find and cut to length two 0-80 screws to mount the crankpins to their respective parts. The head of the screw should be big enough to capture the bearing on the pin. If not, then a washer will need to be included. In either case, make sure the diameter is no bigger than the inner race OD so that there is no possibility of the screw head or washer rubbing the bearing shield or outer race. A large beveled washer could also be used as the outer retaining washer.

Displacer and Piston Connecting Rods

Both connecting rods are bent from .032 " dia. music wire. Common to the two is an eye at the upper end to take the bearing rings, a short leg at the other end which serves as the wrist pin, and an offset so that the plane in which the eye lies passes right through the center of the wrist pin section. The offset is there to clear the piston yoke or the displacer rod end as can be clearly seen in the assembly drawings. It is most important also that the axis of the wrist pin leg be exactly perpendicular to the plane of the eye. In other words the axes of the two bearings of the connecting rod must be parallel. When bending the connecting rods, constantly check that these conditions are satisfied. Just holding the rod up for scrutinizing and squinting at it is not good enough. Hold the eye down on a flat block on a surface plate and check the other end with a little square or square block to be sure of the correct alignment.

---

[1] Actually, flanged bearings can be used here as well if a counterbore is made in the bearing rings to clear the flange.

Now the length of the piston connecting rod should be determined from your actual engine. The piston should clear the bottom of the cylinder of course. The actual clearance is not at all critical in this kind of engine so you can be generous. An extra 1/16 or 1/8" of piston clearance hardly adds any dead space that the engine would notice because it has so much already in the relatively large displacer chamber.[1]

Likewise the length of the displacer connecting rod should be determined from the actual engine, but on this rod a "zigzag" bend is recommended to make final adjustment possible. By straightening out the zigzag, or by folding it up more, the rod is made longer or shorter. The idea here is to adjust it until the displacer closely approaches each plate but without actually making contact. Make the bearing rings next and then you can assemble and make this adjustment.

Bearing Rings and Retaining Collars

The bearing rings are turned from Nylon or Delrin so that the bearings snugly push in. The outside features a groove that the eye of the connecting rod snaps into. Actually, the ring can be reduced in diameter on one side of the groove so that it can be easily pushed into the eye until the eye snaps into the groove.

The final parts to be made are the tiny retaining collars. These are beveled Nylon or Delrin washers that are drilled to be a push fit onto the music wire used for the connecting rods. The bevel is an important feature which reduces the friction moment by preventing the large diameter of the retainer from rubbing. The general assembly drawing shows them in place. Position them so that the little end is in line with the big end bearing. Leave a little axial clearance.

Final Assembly and Adjustments

All that remains is to link up the displacer and piston to their respective cranks. Begin with the displacer. Insert the crankshaft into

---

[1] The dead volume just within the regenerator elements is about ten times the entire piston swept volume.

the main bearings with a short spacer between the crankthrow and the main bearing. If you look carefully, this spacer is shown on the main sectional assembly drawing. I made mine by cutting rings from 1/8" OD brass tubing in the lathe with a tiny parting tool. About 1/16" long is right for the displacer side. With the flywheel off, hook up the displacer connecting rod to the displacer rod and to its crankpin. Adjust the connecting rod length by bending the zigzag as described above. The shaft must turn surprisingly freely. You may have to make a longer or shorter shaft spacer to get the alignment just right depending upon the actual dimensions of the parts on your engine. At this point you can put on the balance weight and adjust it as already described.

Now the flywheel can be mounted. Another shaft spacer is needed here to keep the hub from rubbing on the bearing OD or the housing and causing too much friction. It too is shown on the assembly drawing and is about 1/32" long, but again this may have to be adjusted on your particular engine. Assemble the connecting rod to the piston yoke as shown in the drawings. This is best done by removing the yoke from the piston, adjusting the retaining collars to align the rod with a little side play, and then refixing the yoke in the piston. Mount the crankpin on the flywheel hub with the connecting rod big end in place. Check for free rotation with the vent hole open. You can also at this point put a blob of clay on the flywheel to approximately balance the piston weight. Set the two crankpins so that they are at 90° to each other. This is not a critical setting; doing it "by eye" will be close enough.

The engine should now be ready for its first trial. The most convenient heat source for the initial run is a bowl of nice warm tap water. I often use a good size piece of aluminum warmed up by running hot tap water over it. Set the engine on it and let the bottom plate warm up for a minute. Position the flywheel roughly at midstroke and screw in the vent plug sealing up the engine. Gently rotate the flywheel and your engine should soon start running on its own! It may take several or even quite a few rotations of the flywheel depending upon how much air is initially captive within the engine. For best operation the engine must have just enough air inside so that the mean pressure within the engine over a cycle equals the outside atmospheric pressure. This gives the "double acting" or "push-pull" power stroke effect that was described earlier in the book, which is the most efficient way for the engine to operate. Usually the engine fairly quickly and automatically adjusts this by the small amount of leakage past the piston and the displacer rod which is unavoidable. However, if your piston is a really good fit, it may take more time for this adjustment to take place, so you'll have to spin the flywheel half a dozen times or so before it takes off on its own. To help this process along, you can ever so slightly crack open the vent screw and then tighten it down when the engine starts.

If the engine runs much slower than 100 rpm or so on warm water, there is a tight spot in the mechanism or an air leak somewhere that should be traced down and fixed. When all the bugs have been worked out, your N-92 engine will run smoothly and effortlessly when placed on top of your warm hand!

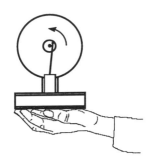

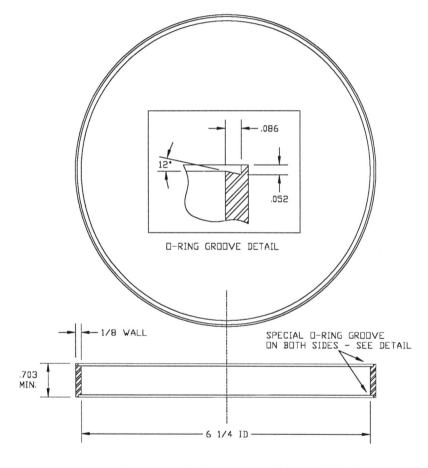

.086

12°

.052

O-RING GROOVE DETAIL

1/8 WALL

SPECIAL O-RING GROOVE
ON BOTH SIDES - SEE DETAIL

.703
MIN.

6 1/4 ID

DISPLACER CHAMBER RING
PLEXIGLAS

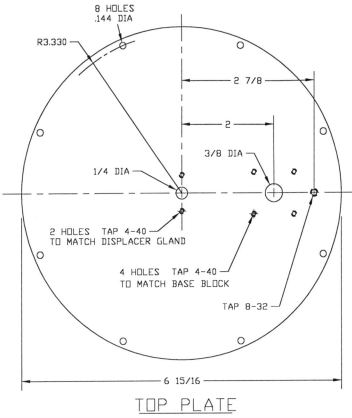

8 HOLES
.144 DIA

R3.330

2 7/8

2

3/8 DIA

1/4 DIA

2 HOLES TAP 4-40
TO MATCH DISPLACER GLAND

4 HOLES TAP 4-40
TO MATCH BASE BLOCK

TAP 8-32

6 15/16

TOP PLATE

1/8 THICK ALUMINUM

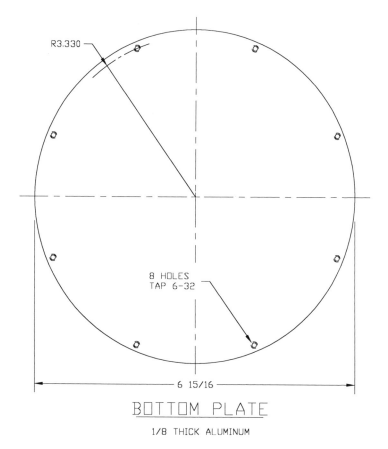

R3.330

8 HOLES
TAP 6-32

6 15/16

BOTTOM PLATE

1/8 THICK ALUMINUM

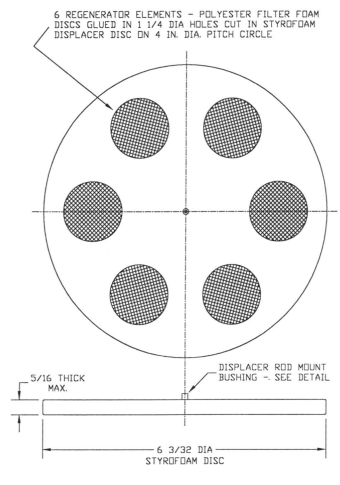

6 REGENERATOR ELEMENTS – POLYESTER FILTER FOAM
DISCS GLUED IN 1 1/4 DIA HOLES CUT IN STYROFOAM
DISPLACER DISC ON 4 IN. DIA. PITCH CIRCLE

DISPLACER ROD MOUNT
BUSHING –. SEE DETAIL

5/16 THICK
MAX.

6 3/32 DIA
STYROFOAM DISC

DISPLACER

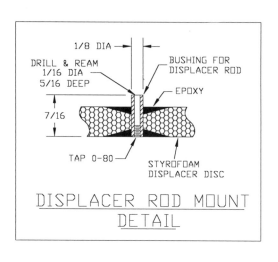

1/8 DIA

DRILL & REAM
1/16 DIA
5/16 DEEP

BUSHING FOR
DISPLACER ROD

EPOXY

7/16

TAP 0-80

STYROFOAM
DISPLACER DISC

DISPLACER ROD MOUNT
DETAIL

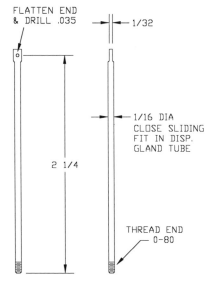

FLATTEN END
& DRILL .035

1/32

1/16 DIA
CLOSE SLIDING
FIT IN DISP.
GLAND TUBE

2 1/4

THREAD END
0-80

DISPLACER ROD
STEEL

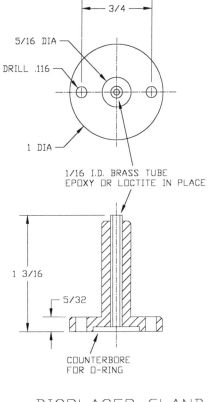

3/4

5/16 DIA

DRILL .116

1 DIA

1/16 I.D. BRASS TUBE
EPOXY OR LOCTITE IN PLACE

1 3/16

5/32

COUNTERBORE
FOR O-RING

DISPLACER GLAND
ALUMINUM

75

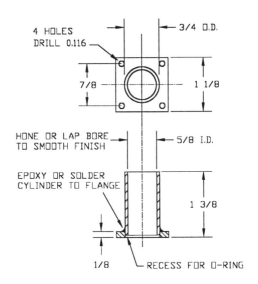

4 HOLES
DRILL 0.116

3/4 O.D.

7/8

1 1/8

HONE OR LAP BORE
TO SMOOTH FINISH

5/8 I.D.

EPOXY OR SOLDER
CYLINDER TO FLANGE

1 3/8

1/8

RECESS FOR O-RING

CYLINDER

BRASS

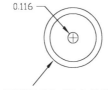

0.116

FINISH O.D. TO A CLOSE
SMOOTH SLIDING FIT
IN CYLINDER BORE

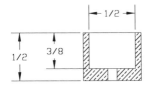

1/2

1/2

3/8

PISTON
GRAPHITE

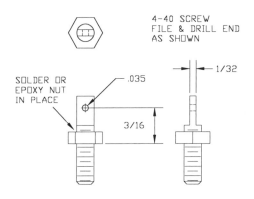

4-40 SCREW
FILE & DRILL END
AS SHOWN

1/32

.035

SOLDER OR
EPOXY NUT
IN PLACE

3/16

PISTON YOKE

BRASS OR STEEL

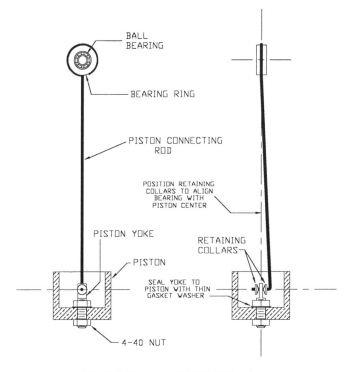

BALL
BEARING

BEARING RING

PISTON CONNECTING
ROD

POSITION RETAINING
COLLARS TO ALIGN
BEARING WITH
PISTON CENTER

PISTON YOKE

RETAINING
COLLARS

PISTON

SEAL YOKE TO
PISTON WITH THIN
GASKET WASHER

4-40 NUT

PISTON ASSEMBLY

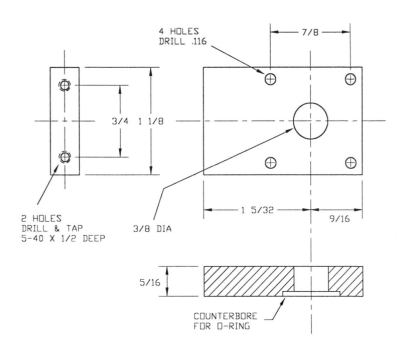

4 HOLES
DRILL .116

7/8

3/4 1 1/8

2 HOLES
DRILL & TAP
5-40 X 1/2 DEEP

3/8 DIA

1 5/32

9/16

5/16

COUNTERBORE
FOR O-RING

BASE BLOCK
ALUMINUM

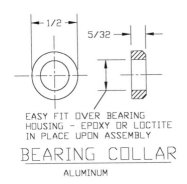

1/2

5/32

EASY FIT OVER BEARING
HOUSING - EPOXY OR LOCTITE
IN PLACE UPON ASSEMBLY

BEARING COLLAR
ALUMINUM

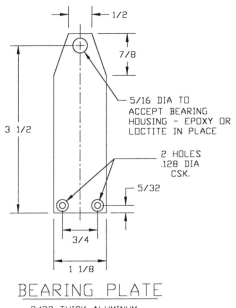

1/2

7/8

5/16 DIA TO
ACCEPT BEARING
HOUSING - EPOXY OR
LOCTITE IN PLACE

3 1/2

2 HOLES
.128 DIA
CSK.

5/32

3/4

1 1/8

BEARING PLATE

3/32 THICK ALUMINUM

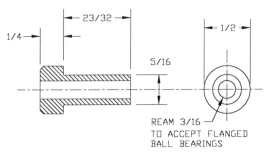

23/32

1/4

5/16

1/2

REAM 3/16
TO ACCEPT FLANGED
BALL BEARINGS

BEARING HOUSING

ALUMINUM

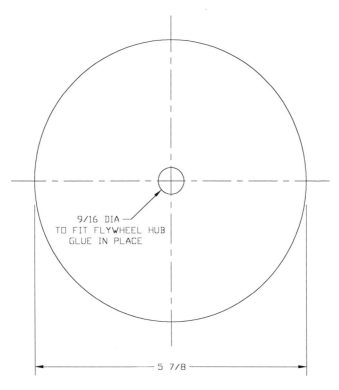

9/16 DIA
TO FIT FLYWHEEL HUB
GLUE IN PLACE

5 7/8

FLYWHEEL

1/16 THICK PLEXIGLAS

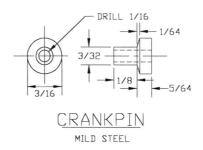

DRILL 1/16

1/64

3/32

3/16

1/8

5/64

CRANKPIN

MILD STEEL

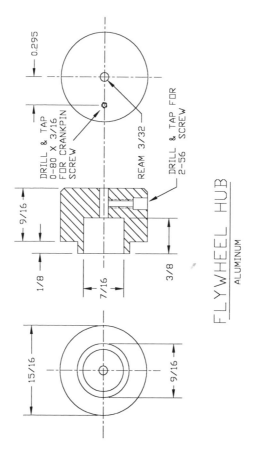

0.295

DRILL & TAP
0-80 X 3/16
FOR CRANKPIN
SCREW

REAM 3/32

DRILL & TAP FOR
2-56 SCREW

9/16

1/8

7/16

3/8

15/16

9/16

FLYWHEEL HUB
ALUMINUM

81

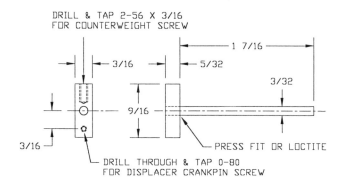

DRILL & TAP 2-56 X 3/16
FOR COUNTERWEIGHT SCREW

3/16

5/32

1 7/16

3/32

9/16

3/16

PRESS FIT OR LOCTITE

DRILL THROUGH & TAP 0-80
FOR DISPLACER CRANKPIN SCREW

CRANKSHAFT
STEEL

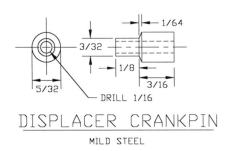

1/64

3/32

1/8

5/32

3/16

DRILL 1/16

DISPLACER CRANKPIN
MILD STEEL

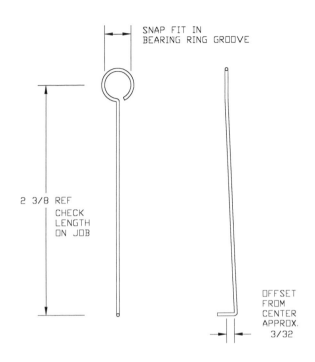

SNAP FIT IN
BEARING RING GROOVE

2 3/8 REF
CHECK
LENGTH
ON JOB

OFFSET
FROM
CENTER
APPROX.
3/32

PISTON CONNECTING ROD

.032 DIA. MUSIC WIRE

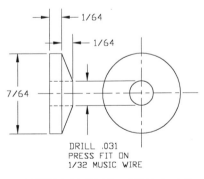

1/64

1/64

7/64

DRILL .031
PRESS FIT ON
1/32 MUSIC WIRE

RETAINING COLLAR

NYLON OR DELRIN

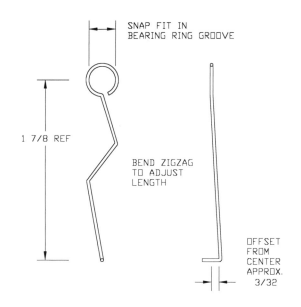

SNAP FIT IN
BEARING RING GROOVE

1 7/8 REF

BEND ZIGZAG
TO ADJUST
LENGTH

OFFSET
FROM
CENTER
APPROX.
3/32

DISPLACER CONNECTING ROD

.032 DIA. MUSIC WIRE

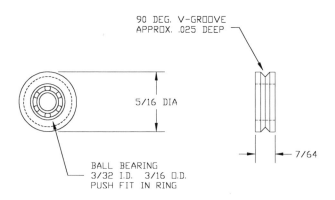

90 DEG. V-GROOVE
APPROX. .025 DEEP

5/16 DIA

BALL BEARING
3/32 I.D. 3/16 O.D.
PUSH FIT IN RING

7/64

BEARING RING

NYLON OR DELRIN

REFERENCES

The following is a list of all the books, technical papers, and articles specifically referred to in this book. They will provide the reader with more information on the topics introduced in the text and furnish additional references for further study.

Books

An Introduction to Stirling Engines by J. R. Senft, 1993, Moriya Press, P.O.Box 384, River Falls WI 54022

Ringbom Stirling Engines by J. R. Senft, 1993, Oxford University Press, 200 Madison Ave., New York NY 10016

Stirling Motor: history-theory-practice by Ivo Kolin, 1991, Zagreb University Publications Ltd., Croatia

Isothermal Stirling-Cycle Engine by Ivo Kolin, 1983, University of Zagreb Press, Croatia

Technical Papers

Low Temperature Differential Stirling Engines

"An ultra low temperature differential Stirling engine" , J. R. Senft, <u>Proc. 5th International Stirling Engine Conference</u> , Paper #ISEC 91032, Dubrovnik, May, 1991.

"A direct solar Stirling engine", J.R. Senft, 1987, <u>Jour. Washington Academy of Sciences</u> , Vol. 77, No.4, p.183-189.

"Recent development of the flat plate Stirling engine" , Ivo Kolin ,1986, <u>Proc. 21st Intersociety Energy Conversion Engineering Conference</u> , Paper #869113,   American Chemical Society, San Diego, August.

"A solar Ringbom Stirling engine", J. R. Senft, 1986, <u>Proc. 21st Intersociety Energy Conversion Engineering Conference</u> , Paper #869112, American Chemical Society, San Diego, August.

"Investigation of the potential of a direct solar Stirling engine", J. R. Senft, 1986, Final Report to the Charles A. Lindbergh Fund, Minneapolis.

"A low temperature difference Ringbom Stirling demonstration engine", J. R. Senft, 1984, <u>Proc. 19th Intersociety Energy Conversion Engineering Conference</u> , Paper #849126, American Nuclear Society, San Francisco.

"Low temperature difference Stirling engine" Ivo Kolin, 1984, <u>Proc. 19th Intersociety Energy Conversion Engineering Conference</u> , Paper #849029, American Nuclear Society, San Francisco.

Mechanical Efficiency

"Mechanical efficiency considerations in the design of an ultra low temperature differential Stirling engine" , J. R. Senft, <u>Proc. 27th Intersociety Energy Conversion Engineering Conference</u> , SAE Paper # 929024, San Diego, August,1992.

"Brake performance potential of Crossley-Stirling engines" , J. R. Senft, 1991, <u>Proc. 26th Intersociety Energy Conversion Engineering Conference</u> , Paper #910314, American Nuclear Society , Boston, August.

"Mechanical efficiency of kinematic heat engines", J. R. Senft, 1987, <u>Jour. Franklin Institute</u> , Vol. 324, No.2, p.273-290.

"Limits on the mechanical efficiency of heat engines", J. R. Senft, 1987, <u>Proc. 22nd Intersociety Energy Conversion Engineering Conference</u> , Paper #879071, American Institute of Aeronautics and Astronautics, Philadelphia, August.

"Mechanical efficiency of Stirling engines - general mathematical considerations", J. R. Senft, 1985,   <u>Proc. 20th Intersociety Energy Conversion Engineering Conference</u> , Paper #859436, Society of Automotive Engineers, Miami, August.

Articles

"A Stirling Engine of the First Degree", J. R. Senft, <u>Modeltec Magazine,</u> P. O. Box 1226, St. Cloud MN 56302, October, 1995.

"A bell ringer for low temperature differential Stirling engines" , J. R. Senft, <u>Modeltec Magazine,</u> P. O. Box 1226, St. Cloud MN 56302, December, 1997.

"Domino - a miniature low temperature differential Stirling engine" , J. R. Senft, <u>Modeltec Magazine,</u> P. O. Box 1226, St. Cloud MN 56302, December, 1998.

"Hot Air Stateside", Mick Fox, <u>Model Engineer Magazine,</u> 1 November 1991, pp532-533.

"New record low temperature difference Stirling engine", <u>Stirling Machine World Newsletter,</u> June, 1990.

"Fitting Cylinders and Pistons" , J. R. Senft, <u>Live Steam Magazine</u> , September, 1979, pp 14-16.

"A Short Course in Lapping" , J. R. Senft, <u>Live Steam Magazine</u> , October, 1979, pp 26-29.

SOURCES

Airpot Corporation , 35 Lois St., Norwalk CT 06851. Phone (203) 846-2021. FAX (203) 849-0539. Manufacturers of glass cylinder and graphite piston units. The Airpot unit used on N-92 is their "Model 160 super fit piston/cylinder assembly: 1.500" long cylinder with cylinder head 100-02 and no rod" If you wish to experiment with longer strokes, there is room to accommodate a 2.00" long cylinder instead.

Bailey Craftsman Supply, P. O. Box 276, Fulton MO 65251-0276. Phone (573) 642-5998. An extensive line of engines, kits, books and videos on Stirling engines. www.baileycraft.com

New Machine Company, 12121 NE 66th Street, Kirkland WA 98033. Model Stirling engines and books.

Nordex , 50 Newtown road, Danbury CT 06810-6216. Phone (800) 243-0986. Suppliers of miniature ball bearings and other mechanical components. The bearings required for N-92 are two each of ABS-A6-10 (flanged) and ABS-A1-38 (plain).

Stock Drive Products, 55 South Denton Ave., New Hyde Park NY 11040. Phone (516)328-3300. Suppliers of ball bearings and other mechanical components. The bearings required for N-92 are two each of A 7Y55-FSS1809. (flanged) and A 7Y55-PSS1809 (plain).

Small Parts Inc., 13980 N. W. 58th Court, P. O. Box 4650, Miami Lakes FL 33014-0650. Phone (800) 220-4242. Suppliers of materials, nylon fasteners, tools, mechanical components, and books.

Stirling Machine World , 8880 N. Duskfire Dr., Tucson AZ 85737-2366. In addition to publishing a quarterly newsletter on Stirling engines, this company sells models, a complete line of books, and can supply reprints of technical papers.

OTHER BOOKS FROM MORIYA PRESS

An Introduction to Stirling Engines
James R. Senft

This book covers the subject of hot air engines and their modern counterparts from the beginning. In an easy to read style, this book starts with the elementary ideas that underlie all heat engines and builds up to clear descriptions of how Stirling engines work. Each of the major types of Stirling engine is specifically covered and fully explained, starting with the simplest and proceeding to the more complex. The book contains 60 drawings and photographs illustrating the basic principles of engine operation and showing examples of old, new, and experimental Stirling engines. Anyone interested in engines will find something new in this fresh account of the Stirling. 80 pages. ISBN 0-9652455-0-0. $12.95 postpaid

The Evolution of the Heat Engine
Ivo Kolin

This book traces the development of present day engines and related thermal machines from their origins in the past. It features large detailed drawings which show all the essential working details of an incredible variety of historical engines. The book contains technical data on each engine and many direct quotations of the inventors and pioneers of these devices. Coverage includes the Stirling, Wankel, Diesel, Otto-Langen, Ericsson, Cayley-Buckett, Lenoir, Papin, Savery, Newcomen, and Watt. Gas turbine development is thoroughly described. Little known engines such as Malone's liquid engine are also illustrated. Even rockets are analyzed as heat engines covering their development from Tsiolkovsky and Goddard to Apollo 11. The book also covers cooling machines including the modern Philips air liquefier and the older Giffard and Windhausen cold air engines. Large format. 106 pages. ISBN 0-9652455-2-7. $21.95 postpaid.

Order from your favorite bookseller or direct from

Moriya Press
P. O. Box 384
River Falls WI 54022